LYLE

ANTIQUES
PRICE GUIDE
1999

PERIOD LIVING
& TRADITIONAL HOMES

First published in 1998

1 3 5 7 9 10 8 6 4 2

Ebury Press
Random House, 20 Vauxhall Bridge Road, London SW1V 2SA

Random House Australia Pty Limited
20 Alfred Street, Milsons Point, Sydney, New South Wales 2061, Australia

Random House New Zealand Limited
18 Poland Road, Glenfield, Auckland 10, New Zealand

Random House South Africa (Pty) Limited
Endulini. 5A Jubilee Road, Parktown 2193, South Africa

Random House UK Limited Reg. No. 954009

A CIP catalogue record for this book is available from the British Library

ISBN 0091865697

Printed and bound in Great Britain by
Caledonian International Book Manufacturing Ltd, Glasgow

The publishers wish to express their sincere thanks to the following for their involvement and assistance in the production of this volume.

TONY CURTIS (Editor)
EELIN McIVOR (Sub Editor)
ANNETTE CURTIS (Editorial)
CATRIONA DAY (Art Production)

ANGIE DEMARCO (Art Production)
NICKY FAIRBURN (Art Production)
SHELLEY HAMILTON
PHILIP SPRINGTHORPE

There has never been a better time to have a look in your local junk shop/flea market, or even your own garage or attic, for the forgotten treasure that could make you seriously rich. 'Pull the other one', do I hear you say? Now that an enormous part of the population regularly tunes in to the Antiques Road Show and all the other antiques awareness programmes it has spawned, can there really be anyone left who doesn't know, to the nearest 50p, the value of absolutely anything they may find tucked away in a cupboard, or happen across at the local church jumble sale?

The answer is a resounding yes!

Let me tell you a story. Once upon a time (about six months ago, actually), there was a dear little chest, which lived in a house in the west of Scotland. One day, its owners decided that it was time to sell it, so they contacted the appropriate agent. Now this was not McWump, McFlannel and MacLueless just down the road, but a Really Big Auction House (the name of which immediately comes to mind whenever you think of a Really Big Auction House). They came and took a look and agreed that it really was a dear little chest, probably a George II reproduction piece, actually, and they would put it in one of their rather more plebeian auction sales, with an estimate of £1,000-£1,500. And all was well, and everyone was happy.

But two American dealers happened to be thumbing through the catalogue for this particular auction, and realised that this dear little chest had very likely been made in Boston in the 18th century, and, if so, was one of only about ten in existence. When they saw the catalogue estimate which had been put on it, they forsook their Thanksgiving turkey, hastily packed a bag, and took the very first flight to Scotland, in the hope of scooping the bargain of the century.

Now, whether the news that two big American players were descending on this very homespun furniture sale reached the Really Big Auction House, or whether some of their own experts in America choked on their cornflakes on reading the catalogue, all manner of red lights began to flash and alarm bells started to ring. The dear little chest was whisked out of the sale at the last minute, and was itself dispatched on a plane to the USA, where it was entered in another, much more glamorous, sale, and ended up fetching $595,000!

The moral to this tale is that even the experts, like Homer, can nod, and that, armed with information of the kind you will find in the *Lyle Antiques Price Guide*, you too will be equipped to recognise that bargain when you see it, and what's more, have a very good idea of the type of thing you should be looking for.

The other thing to remember is that the goalposts are moving all the time. Gone are the days when valuable antiques meant exclusively Ming china, Byzantine bronzes, fine French furniture, and the like - the sort of thing you might see in stately homes, but were very unlikely to find when clearing Auntie Maisie's attic. When the record for a teddy bear stands at £55,000, and a cigarette card can fetch $451,000, you begin to realise that the most unlikely objects can be real money spinners.

So, rule 1 is to know it when you see it, and rule 2 is to be aware of what could, in the future, be worth a small fortune. (The answer to the second rule is that almost anything qualifies, as will be very apparent to you as you browse through these pages.)

If all this sounds too mercenary, then push rule 3 at least one place up the list; which is, the whole business should be enormous *fun!* Few things can equal the excitement of hearing something you've set your heart on knocked down to you at an auction, and gloating over it when you get it home.

If you've decided to start a new collection, then make sure it's of something in which you're interested and enjoy having around, as it's always possible that it might not be *quite* the next item due to take off into the stratosphere. (But of course, if *you* find something fascinating, the chances are that someone else will like it as well.) The words 'sought after' are heard again and again when it comes to collectables, and that's what it really comes down to in the end. The more people who are interested in collecting something, the more its value will rise. The only reason that that teddy bear sold for so much more than any other had fetched before or since, was that two people turned up at the same sale determined to 'bag that bear'!

Every year, as the *Lyle Antiques Price Guide* is published, we report on what has been fetching money in the previous twelve months, and some of the items take a bit of believing. The last two years, for example, have seen the rise and rise of the Pendelfin rabbit, surely the most unlikely of all moneyspinners, the sort of thing you might have bought for a child in a souvenir shop in the 1970s, or something your child might have spent his own pocket money on.

Many people, I venture to say, would find these goofy little creatures totally without intrinsic worth and a bit short on charm as well, and some of their early successes were greeted with gales of laughter in the salerooms. But they have confounded their critics and had the last laugh, as early models continue regularly to fetch sums of £5-600 or more. (The record stands at about £950.)
If you remember that Clarice Cliff used to be a mainstay of Woolworth's china stock, with pieces costing sixpence or so, you begin to get the picture.

Collecting is a compulsive hobby, which can become a way of life. Not only is it great fun and immensely satisfying, as you become ever more knowledgeable about your chosen field, but there is always the teasing possibility that, just waiting for you round the next corner, is the item which could make your fortune. And with the knowledge gained in the 'Lyle Book', you stand a better chance of knowing it when you see it. Good luck and many hours of happy hunting!

EELIN MCIVOR

CONTENTS 5

HISTORICAL FACTS
Advertising Signs

From the Victorian age until about the middle of the 20th century any mass marketing promotions relied heavily upon the use of display advertising signs.

Designed to catch the eye of the passing public their function, then as now, was to make an immediate impact. Most were at least one metre square, brightly coloured and bore a trade emblem.

The most valuable and not surprisingly the most avidly sought by collectors originate from the Art Nouveau and Art Deco periods. The best examples are enamelled on metal but even cardboard signs in good condition from these periods are popular with collectors.

Many famous artists including McKnight Kauffer, Norman & Harry Rountree designed signs for brand name firms such as Oxo, Fry's, Nestle's, Rowntree's and the major petrol and oil companies. Car manufacturers' signs are amongst the most collectible, particularly those for Lagonda, Bentley, Rolls Royce and Bugatti.

A 19th century Dresden group advertising Yardley's Old English Lavender, depicting a mother and two children carrying baskets of lavender, 12in. high.
(H.C. Chapman & Son) £430 $675

Guinness advertising enamel sign, rectangular, depicting the drayman, 51cm. high. (Christie's) £130 $208

A set of three Carltonware Guinness advertising toucans painted in black, white, yellow, red and peach, graduating from 10in. to 6½in.
(Christie's) £200 $320

An enamel sign for Singer sewing machines, in seven colours, by the Frankfurt Enamel Works, 58 x 88cm. (Auction Team Köln) £136 $218

Marius Rossillon (O'Galop), Nunc est Bibendum, lithograph in colours, 1896, printed by Cornille & Serre, Paris, backed on linen, 61 x 46in.
(Christie's) £6,325 $10,120

Guinness Time, an advertising pocket watch, the face inscribed and printed with a smiling pint.
(Christie's) £460 $730

An Allcock fishing tackle display board for the International Fisheries Exhibition 1883, Bronze Medal winner for a 'General Collection of Fishing Tackle', 31in. high.
(Christie's) £1,955 $3,216

HISTORICAL FACTS
Aeronautical

The honour of being first in the air belongs to America – the first aeroplane was invented by Samuel Pierpoint Langley in 1896 and the first powered flight was made in 1903 by the Wright brothers. Since those early days enthusiasts have vied to possess relics of flight. Books, photographs, log books, airmail letters, posters and even bits of old planes are all collected. The field is enormous, ranging from autographs or photographs of famous flying aces like Amy Johnson, Jim Mollison, Douglas Bader, Sheila Scott and space age astronauts, to ashtrays and cigarette lighters made in the shape of aeroplanes or zeppelins. Most old aeroplanes are held in museums or in historical collections but there are a few enthusiasts, especially in America, who are rich and daring enough to buy old aircraft and even to fly them. More cautious collectors however confine themselves to collecting a variety of plane parts such as wooden propellers or safer still airline baggage tickets.

A D.H.4 four-bladed propeller, WWI period, tips with green-painted brass sheaths, boss with circular mirror, 120½in. diameter.
(Sotheby's)   £1,150 $1,875

A U.S. type G-1 flying jacket, by Ralph Edwards Sptswear, Inc., the back with artwork entitled *The Great Speckled Bird*.
(Sotheby's)   £759 $1,237

A 1940 Air Ministry bell, cast with Crown, initials and date, with clapper and attached to wrought iron bracket, bell 10¾in. diameter.
(Sotheby's)   £805 $1,361

Winston S. Churchill, signed B.E.A. silver wing menu, 25th September 1952, obtained when Churchill was flying to Nice by one of the cabin crew.
(Vennett-Smith)   £300 $495

A wheel believed to be from H.M. Airship No. 1, 'The Mayfly', circa 1911, in mahogany with cast metal spokes and frame, 28in. wide overall, sold with a period photograph.
(Sotheby's)   £5,520 $9,218

A Luftwaffe summer weight flying helmet, with original label, complete with throat microphone, and a pair of 'Leitz' pattern goggles.
(Sotheby's)   £172 $287

A WWII R.A.F. operations room clock, by F.W. Elliott Ltd., dial with crest and red, purple and yellow 5 minute sectors, dated 1939, with pendulum.
(Sotheby's)   £1,265 $2,062

An Egyptian polychrome painted cartonnage mummy mask of a female, with central frontal uraeus, Late Period after 500 B.C., 17in. high.
(Bonhams)   £1,800 $2,988

A marble Janus-head, with the face of a youth on one side and a bearded man on the other, Roman, 10¼in. high.
(Bonhams)   £3,000 $4,770

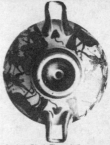

An Attic Black-Figure kylix, decorated around the exterior with, on one side, Hercules, 5th century B.C., 2¾in. high.
(Bonhams)   £1,900 $3,021

TOP TIPS

When buying at auction remember that you are buying the item as seen with all its faults and imperfections and you are deemed to have satisfied yourself as to the articles condition and originality. Make time therefore to read the catalogue description carefully and view the auction at a time when you are under no pressure – ten minutes before the sale is not a good idea!

THE CLOCK HOUSE

An Egyptian bronze striding Apis bull with sun disc and uraeus between the horns, Late Period, after 500 B.C., 3in. long.
(Bonhams)   £400 $645

An Etruscan pottery amphora decorated on both sides of the neck with a grazing stag, circa 6th century B.C., 14¾in. high.
(Bonhams)   £4,200 £6,773

A small Roman marble funerary stele carved with a scene showing a draped reclining man holding out a wreath to a seated draped female, circa 1st-2nd century A.D., 12 x 8⅝in.
(Bonhams)   £550 £913

A Lucanian Red-Figure bell krater decorated on side A with a draped female standing before an altar, 4th century B.C., 11⅝in. high.
(Bonhams)   £1,600 $2,656

An Egyptian granite fragment from a seated royal figure, with a hieroglyphic inscription of one of the Ramesside Kings, New Kingdom, 19th–20th Dynasty, circa 1292–1075 B.C., 12⅛in. high.
(Bonhams)   £1,300 $2,067

An etched half-armour in the style of the third quarter of the 16th century, close helmet, of pronounced 'sparrow's beak' form with stepped centrally divided vision slit, all in the south German style, on a wooden stand. (Sotheby's)
£3,600 $5,888

A composite German armour, mid-16th century, comprising collar, breast-plate, a skirt lame (replaced), movable gussets, early 16th century Italian tassets. (Sotheby's)   £3,910 $6,256

A German black-and-white infantry armour, circa 1560, with associated burgonet of mid-17th century construction. (Sotheby's)   £4,560 $7,475

A German cuirassier armour of blackened steel, circa 1620-30, outer edges turned and predominantly plain throughout. (Sotheby's)   £11,925 $19,550

An English pikeman's composite armour, mid-17th century, including pot helmet formed in two halves joined by a low comb. (Sotheby's)   £2,806 $4,600

A full armour in German Maximilian style, 19th century, hinged visor embossed with a grotesque mask in the manner of Konrad Seusenhofer of Innsbruck. (Sotheby's)   £8,418 $13,800

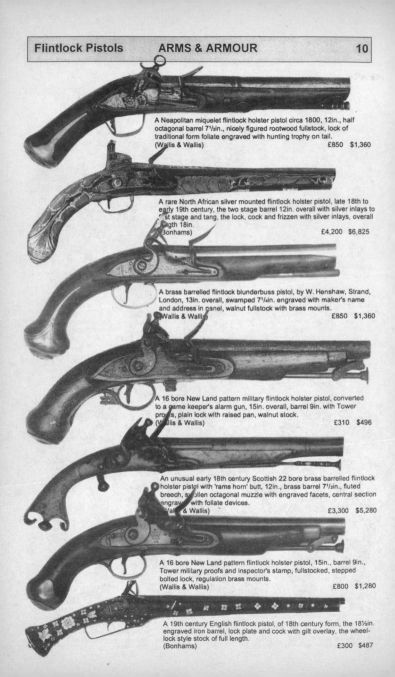

A Neapolitan miquelet flintlock holster pistol circa 1800, 12in., half octagonal barrel 7½in., nicely figured rootwood fullstock, lock of traditional form foliate engraved with hunting trophy on tail.
(Wallis & Wallis)   £850 $1,360

A rare North African silver mounted flintlock holster pistol, late 18th to early 19th century, the two stage barrel 12in. overall with silver inlays to first stage and tang, the lock, cock and frizzen with silver inlays, overall length 18in.
(Bonhams)   £4,200 $6,825

A brass barrelled flintlock blunderbuss pistol, by W. Henshaw, Strand, London, 13in. overall, swamped 7¼in. engraved with maker's name and address in panel, walnut fullstock with brass mounts.
(Wallis & Wallis)   £850 $1,360

A 16 bore New Land pattern military flintlock holster pistol, converted to a game keeper's alarm gun, 15in. overall, barrel 9in. with Tower proofs, plain lock with raised pan, walnut stock.
(Wallis & Wallis)   £310 $496

An unusual early 18th century Scottish 22 bore brass barrelled flintlock holster pistol with 'rams horn' butt, 12in., brass barrel 7½in., fluted breech, swollen octagonal muzzle with engraved facets, central section engraved with foliate devices.
(Wallis & Wallis)   £3,300 $5,280

A 16 bore New Land pattern flintlock holster pistol, 15in., barrel 9in., Tower military proofs and inspector's stamp, fullstocked, stepped bolted lock, regulation brass mounts.
(Wallis & Wallis)   £800 $1,280

A 19th century English flintlock pistol, of 18th century form, the 18½in. engraved iron barrel, lock plate and cock with gilt overlay, the wheel-lock style stock of full length.
(Bonhams)   £300 $487

TOP TIPS

*Collectors and Dealers always prefer to buy items of Militaria in 'as found Condition'.

*Never be tempted to clean metal or other parts of an item as this could destroy the original finish or patination. Many gun parts were originally browned or blued.

*Never handle sword blades or attempt to dismantle Japanese swords. Parts of the sword are delicate and require specialist treatment.

*When buying antique weapons check that all parts match (that decoration is en-suite). Metals used will generally also match e.g. On a pistol, silver trigger guard, silver side plate, silver but-cap and ramrod pipes.

*Never dry-fire a gun (cock and release the hammer) as this can cause damage.

*Never attempt to load or fire a weapon as metal parts can become fatigued with age and old wooden stocks can shatter. You would also be breaking the law!

*If you discover and old gun contact a specialist dealer/auctioneer to find out what you have, NEVER be tempted to sell it to a friend, you could be in breach of the law and liable to a stiff penalty. Ignorance is no defence. Illegal possession of a firearm can result in arrest and imprisonment.

*Always seek specialist advice on old weapons - a mark or a number may hold the key to the weapon's history

*If there is any history uniquely linked to an item this will enhance its value.

Garth Vincent

A Nazi Police shako, green cloth covered body, patent leather crown and peaks, large metal eagle helmet plate.
(Wallis & Wallis)   £190 $304

A fine Prussian Garde du Corps officer's helmet, circa 1900, polished tombac skull with nickel edges, silver-plated parade eagle.
(Sotheby's)   £4,600 $7,498

An other rank's black patent leather lance cap of The 16th (The Queens) Lancers, cloth sides to top, yellow and red silk band, yellow braid, brass mounts.
(Wallis & Wallis)   £270 $432

A 16th century Turkish Turban helmet of gently panelled conical form, the spherical knop with 2 bands of 'damascened' calligraphy and motifs. (Graves Son & Pilcher)
    £5,500 $8,635

A French dragoon trooper's helmet, Third Republic, brass skull with raised comb with Medusa head and felt band printed in leopard skin design.
(Sotheby's)   £805 $1,312

An Imperial Baden Infantryman's Pickelhaube, brass helmet plate spike and mounts, leather chinstrap.
(Wallis & Wallis)   £175 $280

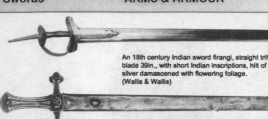

An 18th century Indian sword firangi, straight trifullered single edged blade 39in., with short Indian inscriptions, hilt of traditional form later silver damascened with flowering foliage.
(Wallis & Wallis)   £200 $318

A scarce pre 1881 bandsman's sword of The 32nd (Duke of Cronwall's Light Infantry) Regiment, straight shallow diamond section blade 21in., brass cruciform regulation hilt with 32 and bugle in relief on quillon block.
(Wallis & Wallis)   £100 $160

A 19th century African Ngala tribal executioner's sword, sickle shaped blade 17in. with incised decoration.
(Wallis & Wallis)   £120 $199

A Continental brass hilted sidearm circa 1830, spatulate blade 19in., plain reversed crosspiece, bear's head pommel with fur patterned grip.
(Wallis & Wallis)   £135 $216

A scarce 17th century Indian sword Khanda, broad swollen double edged 27in. reinforced along one edge, steel hilt, finely pierced guard.
(Wallis & Wallis)   £450 $746

A 17th century German Thirty Years War period rapier, broad double edged blade 34½in. deeply struck on both sides with three king's heads, and .:IAHANNI:. in the short fullers, two shell guards.
(Wallis & Wallis)   £1,050 $1,680

A Turkish kilitch, the hilt and scabbard decorated with corals and semi-precious stones, Turkish blade with gold koftgari overlay, 27½in.
(Bonhams)   £4,200 $6,825

A Venetian 'Schiavona' type sword, circa 1780, with superb parcel gilt silver pommel and original silver binding with leather cover for ricasso, blade 34½in.
(Bonhams)   £1,100 $1,787

A good post 1902 Royal Navy Engineer Commander's full dress uniform, comprising: Officer's bi-corn hat, tail coat, epaulettes, and sword belt.
(Bosleys) £300 $480

WWII issue Civil Defence Ambulance driver's tunic, attributed to the County of Yorkshire, to the left breast pocket a crowned CD embroidered badge.
(Bosleys) £145 $232

WAAF issue uniform, worn by a sergeant wireless operator, service dress peaked cap, service dress four pocket tunic with sergeant chevrons. (Bosleys) £260 $416

City of London Yeomanry Rough Riders trooper's uniform, blue grey material with purple facings to the plastron front.
(Bosleys) £385 $616

WWII period US Marine Corps uniform & equipment, comprising steel M1 helmet, herringbone stitched jacket, matching trousers and combat service boots.
(Bosleys) £175 $280

A good post 1902 Royal Horse Guards trooper's helmet, tunic cuirass, silvered skull with brass and silvered King's Crown helmet plate to front.
(Bosleys) £1,300 $2,080

Harry Houdini, signed 5 x 7in., head and shoulders with surname only.
(Vennett-Smith) £580 $957

Richard Nixon, signed and inscribed 8½ x 6in., head and shoulders.
(Vennett-Smith) £90 $149

Ernest Shackleton, signed postcard, full-length in Arctic clothing.
(Vennett-Smith) £140 $230

Robert Baden Powell, signed postcard, head and shoulders as Chief Scout.
(Vennett-Smith) £160 $264

Mikhail Gorbachev, signed 7 x 5in., head and shoulders holding pen.
(Vennett-Smith) £170 $280

Winston S. Churchill, early signed postcard, Rotary 96A, half-length.
(Vennett-Smith) £740 $1,220

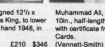

Josephine Baker, signed postcard, head and shoulders.
(Vennett-Smith) £150 $248

George VI, a fine signed 12½ x 17in. sepia photo, as King, to lower border, dated in his hand 1948, in RAF uniform.
(Vennett-Smith) £210 $346

Muhammad Ali, signed colour 8 x 10in., half-length in boxing pose, with certificate from Prince of Cards.
(Vennett-Smith) £130 $215

A running board mounted spare-wheel security carrier trunk with three straps to affix to spare tyre stamped *S.C. Simon & Co. Luggage, Phila; U.S.A.* circa 1912, 25in. diameter.
(Christie's) £1,263 $2,070

Chrysler - a pair of electric headlamps with seal at the top of retaining ring; chrome-plated, pillar mounting; circa 1929, 11in. diameter (Christie's) £98 $161

Carl Benz & Co. – A large early bronze carburettor believed to be from early 2 cylinder engine circa 1894; cylinder choke mechanism.
(Christie's) £345 $562

Jackie Stewart, World Champion Driver 1969,1971 and 1983, a rare original race-suit overall; worn by the driver during the 1969 and 1970 seasons.
(Christie's) £3,680 $5,998

Accident Insurance Coy Ltd., a rare early pictorial advertising showcard for the Commercial Union Assurance Company, colour lithograph, circa 1910, 14 x 18in.
(Christie's) £517 $843

James Hunt, Marlboro McLaren World Champion 1976; an original race-used overall suit worn by James Hunt during the 1976 season.
(Christie's) £6,900 $11,247

Drew and Sons 'En Route' – original picnic set for 4 persons, complete and contained in wicker case. (Christie's) £517 $843

Rolls Royce, a decorative drinks decanter in the form of the famous radiator, by Ruddspeed; chrome-plated with definitive grille, English, circa 1960s.
(Christie's) £253 $412

Ayrton Senna, JPS Lotus 1985 – The original race-suit overalls worn by the driver during the British Grand Prix.
(Christie's) £20,700 $33,741

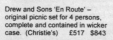

French bronze figure of a winged nymph, signed *E. Laurent*, 19th/20th century, black marble base, 10½in. high. (Skinner) £292 $460

A pair of bronze figures of huntsmen with hounds, cast from models by Alfred Dubucand, French, 19th century, 13½in. high. (Christie's) £1,866 $2,875

A bronze figure of a lion and a serpent cast from a model by Antoine Louis Barye, French, 19th century, 14½in. high, green patina. (Christie's) £1,867 $2,875

A pair of late 19th century Italian bronze figures, Diana Chasseuresse and Apollo Belvedere, after the antique, raised on moulded black marble bases, 16½in. high. (Andrew Hartley) £1,200 $1,920

A late 19th century French bronze figure of the 'Borghese Gladiator, after the Antique, inscribed *Demee Fondeur*, 19in. high. (Andrew Hartley) £1,250 $1,962

A South German bronze group of two children riding piggyback, after Leonard Kern, circa 1640, 4½in. high. (Sotheby's) £1,271 $1,955

A pair of 19th century cast metal book ends in the form of books supporting North American Indian figures of boy and girl. (Russell, Baldwin & Bright) £580 $939

Russian bronze equestrian group, 20th century, depicting an officer and a lady astride a horse, 14½in. high. (Skinner) £548 $863

An early Victorian mother-of-pearl and abalone shell bowfront tea caddy, decorated all-over with a geometric pattern, 9in. wide.
(Christie's) £1,265 $2,100

A Georgian mahogany and line inlaid knife box, the hinged sloping lid with oval silver-mounted escutcheon, 12¼in. high.
(Christie's) £218 $349

A rare Charles II stumpwork casket, English, 17th century, the hinged rectangular top opening to a well, 11¾in. wide.
(Sotheby's) £1,754 $2,875

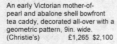

Blue painted firkin, C.&A. Wilder, South Hingham, Massachusetts, 19th century, 10in. high.
(Skinner) £467 $747

French gilt metal cased travelling tea set, early 20th century, by Maquet, comprising two teapots, four spoons, tongs, burner, tea caddy and two Nymphenburg porcelain teacups and saucers.
(Skinner) £326 $518

A George III serpentine mahogany knife box, with brass carrying handle and lock plate, 13¾in. high.
(Andrew Hartley) £280 $439

Interesting Continental marquetry tea caddy, circa 1870, with faceted sides and corners, inlaid with scenes of putti at various pursuits, 4½in. high.
(Skinner) £144 $230

Matched set of three New England ovoid pantry boxes, 19th century, in ash, unpainted old brown colour, 8½in., 9in. and 9½in. long.
(Eldred's) £207 $341

A late Georgian rolled paper hexagonal shaped tea caddy, the hinged lid and sides onlaid with coloured paper scrolls decorated with flowering foliage, 8¼in. wide.
(Christie's) £552 $916

Leica II Luxus no. 94553, lizard-skin body covering and a Leitz nickel 'push-push' Elmar f/ 3.5 50mm. lens. (Christie's) £8,625 $13,024

Black Expo camera, Expo Camera Co., New York; with viewfinder. (Christie's) £517 $842

Leica 72 [18 x 24] no. 357167, chrome, swinging viewfinder mask and a Leitz chrome Elmar 3.5cm. f/3.5 lens. (Christie's) £13,800 $20,838

Hologon Ultrawide no. VK 10-29, Zeiss Ikon, Germany; with a Carl Zeiss Hologon f/ 8 15mm. lens, specially prepared for use in very cold temperatures. (Christie's) £4,830 $7,389

Ergo camera no. 460570, Contessa-Nettel, Germany; 4½ x 6cm., with a Carl Zeiss, Jena Tessar f/4.5 5.5cm. lens no. 542147. (Christie's) £1,265 $2,061

Le Photosphère no. 1854, Compagnie Française de Photographie, Paris; 9 x 12cm. metal body, with helically-focusing lens and magazine back. (Christie's) £805 $1,312

A Premo View mahogany and brass-mounted folding camera by Rochester Optical, for 8 x10 in. prints, 1900. (Auction Team Köln) £242 $382

A Lancaster aluminium mounted Instantograph Patent mahogany and aluminium camera. (Auction Team Köln) £334 $528

Compass II no. 1764, Le Coultre et Cie, Switzerland; with a CCL3B Anastigmat f/ 3.5 35mm. lens, in maker's blue-leather slipcase. (Christie's) £1,610 $2,624

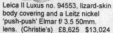

Nikon I no. 609419, chrome, 24 x 32mm., the base plate engraved *Made in Occupied Japan* and with a Nippon Kogaku Nikkor-H-C f/ 2.5cm. lens. (Christie's) £10,925 $17,480

A Mickey Matic Version 1, a Child Guidance product, for 126 film, works by depressing the ears. (Auction Team Köln) £91 $144

A Leica IC secret camera in the form of a book, working by depressing the back of the book, 1931. (Auction Team Köln) £2,424 $3,830

HISTORICAL FACTS
Doulton

The Doulton story began in 1815, when John Doulton, known as the 'best thrower of pint pots in London' set up a pottery business in partnership with a widow called Jones and a journeyman called Watts. The Watts Doulton part of the association continued until the former's retiral in 1853.

In 1835 John's second son Henry joined the company. It was Henry who responded to an approach by John Sparkes head of the newly established Lambeth School of Arts requesting that some of his students should try potting. He set up a pottery studio in a corner of the works, and it is worth noting that George Tinworth and the Barlows, Arthur, Florence and Hannah, were among the first intake.

Henry also acquired an earthenware factory in Burslem, which he renamed Doulton and Co.

Experimentation and constant development were the keynotes for both establishments and they attracted terrific resources of talent. Charles J Noke, for example, joined the company in 1889 and finally became Artistic Director at Burslem. He experimented with Copenhagen and Sèvres type wares and in recreating oriental techniques. The results of the latter were the renowned Flambé , Sung, Chinese jade and Chang pottery. Under Noke, too, the company embarked on one of its most successful lines of all, figure models, the first of which were exhibited at Chicago in 1893.

Susie Cooper coffee service, decorated with abstract design of circles with tails, four cups, seven saucers, cream jug and coffee pot. (G.A. Key) £70 $109

A large glazed earthenware cat, designed by Louis Wain, 1920s, hollow to form a vase, 10in. high. (Christie's) £2,300 $3,749

A 19th century pair of ironstone vases, of lobed baluster form with twin shoulder handles, painted in an Oriental design in Imari palette. 30.5cm. (Bristol) £2,900 $4,640

Robinson & Leadbeater white parian bust of Charles Sumner, England, circa 1880, mounted to raised circular plinth, impressed title, verse and manufacturer's mark, 12⁷/₈in. high. (Skinner) £216 $345

An English delft posset pot and cover, the two handled body divided into three panels of Chinamen, London or Bristol, circa 1730-1740, 19cm. (Tennants) £900 $1,429

Royal Doulton Lambeth Victorian Jubilee ewer of circular baluster form, on a cream foliate and thistle moulded blue reserved ground, impressed marks, 7in. (G.A. Key) £300 $471

A Wade 5in. Disney blow-up model of Jock from Lady and the Tramp, 3¹/₂in. high.
(Anderson & Garland)
£380 $596

A Victorian majolica cheese dish and cover, rustic handle, the domed cover with arched terrace design on a mottled green/brown ground, 23cm. high.
(Wintertons)
£150 $240

A Royal Doulton female figure 'Autumn Breezes', HN1934, 7¹/₂in. high.
(Anderson & Garland)
£74 $117

Bargee teapot, typically moulded with foliage and sprig of flowers, inscribed *Mrs Cornell, Lincoln 1894*, on treacle glazed ground, 8in.
(G A Key)
£110 $176

A pair of Royal Doulton stoneware large baluster vases, each decorated by Frank A. Butler and Bessie Newbery, 40.5cm. high.
(Bearne's)
£1,650 $2,673

Royal Doulton large loving cup, made to celebrate the bi-centenary of Nelson's birth, signed by H. Fenton, 10in.
(G.A. Key)
£600 $954

Blue and white transfer decorated soup tureen with undertray, W.P. & Co., England, circa 1840, 'Maramora' pattern.
(Skinner)
£403 $632

Shorter & Son Ltd. Art Deco pottery jug, formed as a monkey carrying a palm leaf, English, first half 20th century, 11in.
(G.A. Key)
£100 $159

HISTORICAL FACTS
Mantel Clocks

As a basic rule French mantel clocks are nearly all decoration while English models are nearly all clock.

Early French makers to look for are Lepine, Janvier, Amand, Lepaute and Thuret, who started to use a great deal of elaborate scroll-work at the end of the seventeenth century. If you find a clock by any of these makers you have certainly found a good clock. Things to look for are a verge escapement – which is loosely indicated by a horizontally turning crown wheel with sharp teeth just above the pendulum – a painted face or porcelain numerals and a winding hole placed in the face where you least expect it. Pendulums should be pear shaped bobs on brass rods.

The word that really matters in any description is 'ormolu' – that is, it is made of a hard metal, such as brass, which is rough cast before being chiselled and engraved by hand and, finally, coated with a thin amalgam of gold and mercury.

Cheaper nineteenth century mass produced clocks have a similar appearance at first glance, but they are made of spelter. This is a soft metal which is simply cast and gilded. The infallible test is to scratch the underside of the clock; if the gold colour comes away to reveal grey metal, it's spelter, if brass is revealed it is ormolu. Another test is to tap the case sharply with a coin. If the sound is sharp and pingy, you have hard metal; if it is a thud, you have soft.

A gilt-bronze and porcelain mantel clock, Napoleon III, circa 1860, the case cast with a shepherd flanked by panels painted with fruits, 46cm. high.
(Sotheby's)   £2,530 $3,820

A gilt-metal mounted and foliate cut-brass scarlet lacquer striking mantel clock, last quarter 19th century, on toupie feet, 10½in. high.
(Christie's)   £437 $699

Peter Behrens for AEG, Berlin, Synchron double sided electric clock, circa 1910, brass, sheet steel, black painted metal, glass, 14³/₈in. diameter.
(Sotheby's)   £5,520 $8,998

A Napoleon III gilt-bronze and porcelain mantel clock, French, circa 1870, the cover surmounted by a cherub above a revolving annular dial, 87cm. high.
(Sotheby's)   £17,250 $27,082

A gilt-bronze and porcelain mantel clock, Napoleon III, circa 1865, the case cast with a lady and two gallants, 51cm. high.
(Sotheby's)   £4,600 $6,946

A Louis XV style foliate cut-brass inlaid scarlet lacquer and gilt-metal mounted striking mantel clock, last quarter 19th century, waisted case with floral urn finial, 13½in. high.
(Christie's)   £747 $1,195

A 19th century French mantel clock, with eight day movement, in gilt metal oval case with the inset painted porcelain panels, 16in. high.
(Andrew Hartley) £950 $1,492

A Napoleon III Boulle and gilt-bronze bracket clock, Paris, circa 1870, in Louis XV style, the dial above Apollo in his chariot flanked by caryatids, 110cm. high.
(Sotheby's) £3,220 $5,024

A French ormolu mantel clock, of Louis XV design, 19th century, the cylinder movement with outside countwheel, inscribed *Julien LeRoy*, 19¼in. high.
(Christie's) £2,300 $3,818

A French gilt-bronze mounted scarlet lacquer and foliate cut-brass inlaid striking bracket clock, second half 19th century, case surmounted by the figure of an angel with trumpet, 42½in. high.
(Christie's) £2,070 $3,312

Marianne Brandt for Ruppelwerk, Gotha, table clock, circa 1930, black and white painted metal, chromium-plated foot, key, 5⁵/₈in. high. (Sotheby's) £690 $1,125

A Federal inlaid and figured mahogany shelf clock, A. Gooding's, New Bedford, Massachusetts, circa 1800, the arched top with three fluted plinths, 31in. high.
(Sotheby's) £10,465 $16,100

A French porcelain clock on stand, possibly by Michel-Isaac Aaron, mid 19th century, modelled as a Turk on horseback, holding a pistol in his right hand, 21in.
(Bonhams) £2,600 $4,134

A French 19th century enamel and chased gilt lantern shape clock surmounted by a soldier, the watch movement dial painted with a riverscape, 7½in.
(Graves Son & Pilcher) £550 $880

A gilt-bronze and marble mantel clock, Paris, circa 1880, in Louis XVI style, with white enamel dial, mounted within a fluted column, 35cm. wide.
(Sotheby's) £4,025 $6,561

George Prentiss Kendrick copper tea caddy, circa 1892, repoussé foliate design, marked *GPK*, 3¼in. high. (Skinner) £1,438 $2,300

A Georgian bell metal rectangular footman, with turned handles, shaped apron and cabriole front supports, 39½cm. wide. (Bristol) £155 $248

Early 19th century copper samovar of oval form, the four fluted supports moulded with mask designs, 9in. (G.A. Key) £100 $165

Unusual brass dinner gong with horn supports, joined to a domed base, applied throughout with brass mounts, circa late 19th/early 20th century, 13in. (G. A. Key) £125 $200

Unusual Victoria copper tea set, includes teapot, sugar, creamer, and tray, impressed *Victoria, Taxco, Mexico*, coffeepot 8½in. high. (Skinner) £144 $230

Rebajes copper wall plaque, abstract figure of a woman, signed *Rebajes*, 14in. high, 7in. wide. (Skinner) £108 $173

A pierced gilt brass jardinière, early 20th century, of cylindrical form with pierced lattice frieze and moulded base on paw feet, 14in. high. (Christie's) £4,600 $7,383

Copper conical shaped measuring jug. (Chapman Moore & Mugford) £88 $140

A German embossed brass alms dish, 17th century, the centre embossed with bunches of grapes, the border with lozenge decoration, 17½in. diameter. (Bonhams) £280 $448

HISTORICAL FACTS
Bru Dolls

The doll making factory of Bru Jne & Cie was established in 1866 by Casimer Bru. He remained with the company until 1883. It then passed through a series of directorships before amalgamating with a number of other French firms to form the Société Français de Fabrication de Bébés et Jouets (SFBJ) in 1899. Bru dolls, though less costly than their Jumeau counterparts, were luxury items, with bisque heads and composition, wood or kid bodies. Casimer was a great experimenter, and he invented many mechanical devices.

His designs were many and varied and included crying dolls, feeding dolls and two-faced dolls, which showed a happy and a crying or sleeping face.

With regard to bodies, Bru designed types in jointed wood, gusseted and jointed kid and combinations of composition and kid. Early models had bisque shoulder-heads or swivel heads mounted on gusseted kid bodies, and were often adult in shape. These Bru lady dolls tend to have smiling faces with strikingly upturned mouths. The eyes are usually of glass, fringed by long, densely painted lashes.

In 1872 the Bébé Bru line was introduced often with open moulded mouths revealing teeth and tongue. Like other manufacturers of the time, Bru made dolls representing different nationalities. The most common Bru mark is Bru J^{ne} R.

A rare pair of small all-bisque swivel neck character dolls of 'Max & Moritz' probably by J.D Kestner, German, circa 1920, with smiling closed mouths, painted blue eyes, 4¾in. (Sotheby's) £1,552 $2,483

'König Wernicke's lovable black doll', googly eyes, open mouth with two glass teeth, original wig, composition head and body.
(Auction Team Köln) £90 $149

A Louis Vuitton doll, miniature wardrobe trunk and collection of costume, French, circa 1950, of hard plastic, 17in.
(Sotheby's) £1,725 $2,760

A fine Emile Jumeau bisque doll, French, circa 1880, with fixed blue paperweight eyes, open/closed mouth, 23in.
(Sotheby's) £3,910 $6,256

An Oriental Schoenau & Hoffmeister 4900 character with fixed brown slanting eyes, black mohair wig and jointed body, dressed in a kimono, 10in. high.
(Christie's) £483 $781

A rare and unusually large Kammer & Reinhardt googly eyed doll, German, circa 1915, with jointed wood and composition body, 17¼in. (Sotheby's) £7,245 $11,592

A hand-forged puzzle lock, the door of the lock opening when one of the flanking decorations is pushed up, circa 1880.
(Auction Team Köln) £110 $175

A late Victorian Kent's patent knife cleaner, English, late 19th century, on green painted wrought iron stand, 49cm. wide.
(Bonhams) £180 $289

Cast iron washboard with heart cutout, Pennsylvania, 19th century, original surface, 22½ x 12½in.
(Skinner) £1,509 $2,415

Gerhard Marcks for Schott & Gen. Jena'er Glassworks, Jena, coffee machine 'Sintrax' and hot ring, circa 1925, clear, heat-resistant glass, chromium-plated metal, 15¹/₈in.
(Sotheby's) £1,150 $1,875

Bell metal and wood candlemould, Massachusetts, 19th century, the moulded stamped *A.D. Richmond New Bedford, patent*, 10¹/₄in. high.
(Skinner) £506 $805

Designed and executed by Herbert Schulze, Fachhochschule, Dusseldorf, tea maker, 1990, silver-coloured metal, glass, ebony, cork, 11¼in. (Sotheby's) £2,070 $3,374

A large Peugeot coffee grinder, wooden base and cast handle, with brass coffee container, French, circa 1900.
(Auction Team Köln) £155 $246

A Victorian paint-decorated pine birdcage, third quarter 19th century, the demilune-shaped top fitted with a hanging ring, 16in. high.
(Sotheby's) £842 $1,380

A large fan by Marelli, Milan, with brass blades and black cast base, three stage adjustment, 44cm. diameter.
(Auction Team Köln) £89 $141

A very small unusual dress of mushroom and beige coloured silk, labelled *Newberry*, circa 1876-8. (Christie's) £483 $770

A cocktail overdress of black chiffon, embroidered all over with silver bugle beads forming a vermicular pattern, circa 1923. (Christie's) £690 $1,100

A day dress of brown and ivory checked silk, late 1850s, and another of pale blue striped silk, circa 1860. (Christie's) £253 $405

A cocktail dress of black muslin, embroidered with black, silver, ivory and clear beads and sequins, mid 1920s. (Christie's) £437 $700

A cocktail over tunic of jade green crepe embroidered in gold and silver sequins and beads with asymmetrical banding, 1920s. (Christie's) £403 $645

A summer dress en princesse of ecru linen tamboured in ivory silks with stylised floral roundels and foliage, late 1870s. (Christie's) £207 $330

A strapless cocktail dress of bottle green velvet appliqué with black cord and feathers, edged with a tulle frill, labelled *Christian Lacroix, Luxe, Paris*. (Christie's) £250 $400

A cocktail dress of wine coloured chiffon, the skirt embroidered with zigzags in bugle beads, 1920s, and a collar and skull cap. (Christie's) £920 $1,147

The Great Dictator/Le Dictateur
1940, U.A., 16 x 11in.
(Christie's)   £632 $1,043

Breakfast At Tiffany's, 1961,
Paramount, U.S. quad, 30 x 40in.,
linen backed.
(Christie's)   £1,380 $2,277

Casablanca, 1942, Warner Bros.,
15¼ x 11in.
(Christie's)   £1,265 $2,087

Houdini, 1953, Paramount, 22 x
13½in., paper backed.
(Christie's)   £322 $530

A Dog's Life/Une Vie De Chien,
1918, First National, 10¼ x 16½in.
(Christie's)   £575 $950

Brighton Rock, 1947, Associated
British, British one-sheet, 40 x
27in., paper backed.
(Christie's)   £517 $853

Destination Moon/Destination Lune!
1950, Universal, French, 63 x 47in.
linen backed.
(Christie's)   £862 $1,422

It's A Wonderful Life, 1946, R.K.O.,
U.S. title card, 11 x 14in.
(Christie's)   £747 $1,233

Raging Bull, 1980, U.A., advance
U.S. one-sheet, 41 x 27in., linen
backed. (Christie's) £667 $1,100

Grace Kelly, signed 8 x 10in., head and shoulders.
(Vennett-Smith)   £340 $560

Hoffman and Cruise, colour 8 x 10in., from The Rain Man, signed by both Tom Cruise and Dustin Hoffman.
(Vennett-Smith)   £90 $149

Stan Laurel, signed sepia 8 x 10in., head and shoulders.
(Vennett-Smith)   £210 $346

Robert Redford, signed colour 8 x 10in., head and shoulders in evening suit.
(Vennett-Smith)   £70 $115

Bette Davis, signed 7½ x 9in., head and shoulders, from All About Eve, modern reproduction signed in later years.
(Vennett-Smith)   £90 $148

Keanu Reeves, signed colour 8 x 10in., from Speed.
(Vennett-Smith)   £80 $132

Gene Kelly, signed 8 x 10in., head and shoulders in navy uniform, modern reproduction signed in later years.
(Vennett-Smith)   £70 $115

Eddie Murphy, signed colour 8 x 10in., head and shoulders from Coming to America.
(Vennett-Smith)   £60 $100

Audrey Hepburn, signed and inscribed 8 x 10in., head and shoulders.
(Vennett-Smith)   £110 $182

A Hardy black japanned fly box, containing 37 gut-eyed dressed salmon flies, 3 to 6/0 size.
(Christie's) £276 $454

A pike head on a wood shield by Rowland Ward of Piccadilly, with Roland Ward Ltd labels to reverse of shield.
(Bonhams) £340 $547

A Malloch's black japanned salmon fly box, containing 30 gut-eyed and 15 metal-eyed salmon flies.
(Christie's) £264 $434

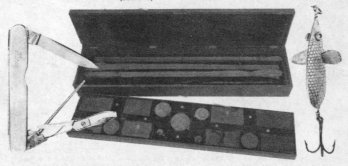

A Hardy's No. 1 angler's knife, with stainless steel blade marked *Howill & Sons, Sheffield*, stiletto and scissors.
(Bonhams) £300 $482

A fine and rare fisherman's brass-bound mahogany tackle case by J. Jones, circa 1850; the lift-out tray with velvet lined compartments, 52½in. long.
(Sotheby's) £10,350 $17,492

A rare late Victorian unnamed glass-eyed spinning bait, attributed to Gregory.
(Bonhams) £340 $547

A rare late Victorian 'Wheeldon' type spinning bait attributed to Gregory, the 2½in. brass lure gilded to the underside.
(Bonhams) £750 $1,206

A fitted brown leather covered tackle case, containing two Ogden Smiths built cane trout fly rods, the base compartments with an Ogden Smiths 'Reversa' net.
(Bonhams) £420 $576

A Hardy Bros. No. 4 angler's knife, with large blade marked *Taylor Sheffield*, screw driver/bottle opener, scissors, tweezers, stiletto, file/discorger, together with a Hardy discorger.
(Bonhams) £220 $354

Trevor Ford, a red Wales International cap v. England, Scotland, Belgium and Ireland, 1949-50.
(Christie's)   £1,265 $2,015

F.A. Cup final, match programme, Chelsea v. Sheffield United, at Old Trafford, Manchester, 24th April 1915. (Christie's) £11,270 $17,947

Noel Cantwell, a green Ireland International cap v. Sweden (2) and Chile, 1959-60.
(Christie's)   £1,207 $1,922

A silver-gilt medal, the obverse inscribed *The Football League, Champions Division 1*, the reverse inscribed *Season 1950-51, L. Bennett*, with ring suspension.
(Christie's)   £3,910 $6,227

A bound volume of The Villa News and Record, Vol.1, No. 45, August 3rd 1907, containing the complete run of forty-five match programmes.
(Christie's)   £2,875 $4,578

A 9ct gold and enamel medal, the obverse inscribed *Scotland v. England, International Football League Match*, the reverse inscribed *J. McMenemy (Celtic)*, lid inscribed *International Football L'ge, Scotland v.England 1913-14*.
(Christie's)   £828 $1,319

A Continental painted bisque porcelain figure of a footballer, the moustached figure shown standing with his arm resting on his hips, possibly German, 23½in. high.
(Christie's)   £2,760 $4,395

A colour photograph of the victorious England World Cup side, 1966, depicting Bobby Moore being held aloft with the trophy in his hands, autographed by the winning team, the image 5¾ x 8¼in.
(Christie's)   £805 $1,282

A red, green and white Wales International jersey, No. 11, autographed by Ryan Giggs.
(Christie's)   £368 $586

HISTORICAL FACTS
Bureaux

The writing desk was born in the monasteries of the Middle Ages, originally as a small, Gothic style oak box with a sloping lid hinged at the back like old fashioned school desk tops.

As time passed and men of letters increased their output, the writing box grew and was made a permanent fixture in the copying rooms of the monasteries, being built upon a stand, usually high enough to be used by a man standing or seated on a high stool.

Later, the hinges of the lid were moved from the back to the front, allowing the lid to fall forward on supports and form a writing platform in the open position. The practice on the Continent was to cover this area with a 'burel' or russet cloth, probably named from the Latin *burrus* (red), the colour of the dye used in its manufacture. It is doubtless from here that we gain the word bureau, though the connotations of the word have changed somewhat since it was first coined.

The bureau remained little more than a box on a stand until the close of the 17th century when it was married to a chest of drawers for obvious practical reasons. From that time onward, there have been few changes in the design beyond relatively small stylistic alterations, which were reflections of the changing tastes of the fashionable rather than modifications dictated by practical usage.

A kingwood and tulipwood crossbanded cylinder desk, of Louis XV style, on slender cabriole supports, 31in. wide.
(Christie's) £747 $1,233

An 18th century Dutch marquetry bureau, the fall front enclosing stepped interior with well.
(Jacobs & Hunt) £3,100 $4,960

A Federal inlaid and figured mahogany slant-front desk, Baltimore, Maryland, circa 1805, the moulded hinged rectangular lid inlaid with a central oval reserve, 39½in. wide.
(Sotheby's) £2,429 $3,737

A Wylie & Lochhead Arts & Crafts oak and stained glass bureau, by E.A. Taylor, two rectangular doors inset with leaded and stained glass panels, 30in. wide.
(Christie's) £10,925 $16,660

Chippendale maple slant lid desk, New England, late 18th century, with a stepped interior of small compartments, flanking a prospect door, 36½in. wide.
(Skinner) £2,893 $4,600

A Chippendale figured walnut slant-front desk, Pennsylvania, circa 1780, the case with four graduated thumbmoulded long drawers, 40in. wide.
(Sotheby's) £2,981 $4,887

HISTORICAL FACTS
Dining Chairs

The Hepplewhite style is renowned for its flowing curves, shield, oval and heart-shaped backs and straight lines broken by carved or painted wheat ears and corn husks, all of which Hepplewhite adapted from the work of Robert Adam, the distinguished architect/ designer and published in his famous guide: *The Cabinet Maker and Upholsterer.*

Though his designs have much in common with those of Hepplewhite, Thomas Sheraton (1751–1806), a drawing master from Stockton on Tees, much preferred straight lines to the curves favoured by Hepplewhite, his chairs achieving their feminine delicacy with their fine turning and slender frames.

Sheraton served his apprenticeship as a cabinet maker but he never actually manufactured furniture himself, concentrating on creating designs which he published in his *Cabinet Maker's and Upholsterer's Drawing Book (1791–1794).* Thomas Chippendale designed and made furniture for the wealthy in his premises in St. Martin's Lane, London, establishing styles of his own rather than copying and adapting those of others. Like Sheraton and Hepplewhite, Chippendale published his designs, which were used by cabinet makers throughout the country, with the result that a considerable number of 'Chippendale' chairs were produced in a variety of qualities and a medley of styles.

A rare William and Mary turned maple upholstered-back side chair, Boston, Massachusetts, 1722–35.
(Sotheby's)   £1,495 $2,300

Two of a set of eight 'Chippendale' mahogany dining chairs, by James Phillips and Sons Ltd. of Bristol.
(Bristol)   (Eight) £960 $1,488

A brace-back Windsor side back, branded *M.BLOOM/N.YORK,* 1787–93, the hooped and moulded crestrail centring nine swelled spindles.
(Christie's)   £1,739 $2,760

Two of a set of six mahogany dining-chairs, of George III design, including two armchairs, on moulded square supports joined by square stretchers.
(Christie's)   (Six) £1,265 $2,024

A good Queen Anne walnut side chair, Pennsylvania, 1730–60, the yoke-form crest above a vase-form splat.
(Sotheby's)   £2,467 $3,795

A pair of Franco-Flemish walnut upholstered armchairs, in Baroque style, on similarly turned legs and stretchers resting on pad feet.
(Sotheby's)   £1,050 $1,680

Gabriel Argy-Rousseau and Bouraine, sculpture 'Papillon', 1928, modelled as a standing female nude, her back arched over her butterfly wings, 10in. (Sotheby's) £25,300 $43,351

Cobalt blue overlay white Peking glass jar and cover, 19th century, carved to one side with an ox beneath a pine tree gazing back at the sun, 5in. high. (Butterfield & Butterfield) £862 $1,380

A large silver-gilt and enamel ornament, by George Frampton, 1898, circular panel depicting a single tree in vibrant blue and green enamels, 3³/₈in. diameter. (Christie's) £9,775 $15,933

Painted cranberry cylindrical gilt metal mounted glass jar, star cut lid and base, raised on three foliate moulded gilt metal paw feet, 7½in. (G.A. Key) £80 $128

Smith Brothers decorated Mount Washington sugar bowl and creamer, ribbed melon-form set with matching yellow centred white aster/daisy like blossoms, 4in. (Skinner) £270 $431

An American silver and cut-glass flask with Columbian Exposition mark, Tiffany & Co., New York, circa 1893, the glass body cut with grapevine and scrolls, 7³/₄in. high. (Sotheby's) £1,121 $1,725

Brilliant cut glass jug, spherical body with offset stoppered spout, applied notched handle in the Sinclaire manner, 7in. high. (Skinner) £327 $518

Emile Gallé, fuchsias vase, circa 1900, yellow glass overlaid with red and etched with flowering stems, 8¼in. (Sotheby's) £2,530 $4,225

A rare enamelled glass jug 'parlant' by Gallé, circa 1900, the body internally streaked with red and green, with an exotic fish, 5½in. high. (Christie's) £5,060 $8,096

Pair of green opaque glass lustres with hanging prism drops, second half 19th century, 12½in. (G.A. Key) £200 $349

An enamelled glass vase, by Gallé, circa 1890, in tinted glass, decorated with sprays of stylised flowers and yellow panels, 6¼in. high. (Christie's) £2,185 $3,561

A carved and internally decorated cameo glass vase, by Ernest Leveille, 1890, the watery grey body internally decorated with patches of sandy yellow and orange, 6⅝in. high. (Christie's) £24,150 $39,364

A leaded glass panel, designed by David Gauld for McCulloch & Co., Glasgow, 1891, the rectangular panel depicting a full-length female figure with auburn hair, 31½ x 18½in. (Christie's) £16,100 $26,404

An enamelled glass vase, by Marcel Goupy, circa 1920, decorated with a frieze of leaping greyhounds against a crazed orange ground, 7⅛in. high. (Christie's) £2,990 $4,874

A carved cameo glass vase by Gallé, circa 1900, heavy flattened body internally streaked with inky blue, overlaid in pale clear amber, pink and aubergine, 6¾in. high. (Christie's) £7,475 $11,137

Pair of Venetian style overlaid glass lustres, the bowls alternately decorated with panels of painted stylised flowers, 19th century, 13in. (G.A. Key) £950 $1,567

Murano Studio glass ritorte coppa, design attributed to Fulvio Bianconi for Venini, oversize brandy snifter form, raised on cobalt blue pedestal stem and foot, 12in. high. (Skinner) £1,092 $1,725

HISTORICAL FACTS
Gramophones

It was Thomas Alva Edison who launched the phonograph in America in 1876 and in 1887 Emile Berliner patented the first gramophone, also in the U.S.A.

The early Edison machine consisted of a box structure housing the works, surmounted by a spindle, a needle lever and a horn. The record in the form of a cylinder, is fitted to the spindle and when the works are cranked up, upon the release of a catch, the cylinder begins to turn, the needle moves onto the cylinder and sound issues from the horn.

The first machines were jerky because of hand cranked powering but in 1896 the techniques of clockwork mechanisms were worked out and shellac discs replaced the old zinc coated rubber discs. From the time of the First World War, every family wanted a gramophone in the parlour and there were many manufacturers vying for their business. They gave their machines wonderful names like Aeolian, Vocalion, Deccalion and Oranoca.

These early machines had big horns, some of which looked very elegant and could be made of brass, painted tin (sometimes decorated with flowers inside), or papier mâché, but as people began to look on the gramophone as a piece of furniture, the horns shrank and were concealed inside the sets which were disguised as cabinets.

A Swiss Paillard Concertola Superfonica portable gramophone, with built in horn and space for discs in lid, circa 1930.
(Auction Team Köln) £122 $194

A Victor III mahogany gramophone with horn by the Victor Talking Machine Co., Camden, NJ.
(Auction Team Köln) £1,561 $2,576

A Klingsor coin-operated gramophone by Krebs & Klenk, Hanau, with concealed integral metal speaker and leaded glass doors, circa 1915.
(Auction Team Köln) £986 $1,627

A Columbia Model 701 standard gramophone, with automatic turn-off, closable speaker front and two side compartments for discs, American, circa 1912, 81cm. wide.
(Auction Team Köln) £366 $582

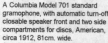

An Edison Bell portable gramophone, the wooden case covered in red paper, with Edison Bell Electrotone sound pick-up, circa 1920.
(Auction Team Köln) £49 $78

A Decca child's portable gramophone with integral speaker, covered and lined with brightly coloured oilcloth, circa 1940.
(Auction Team Köln) £90 $149

A Philips cinema low voltage projection lamp with intergral mirror, 9.4cm. diameter, circa 1950. (Auction Team Köln) £24 $38

Set of mother of pearl barrelled gilt metal opera glasses with handle by Iris of Paris, 19th century, 4in. (G.A. Key) £65 $102

An Exacta six-dial adding machine, in hammered green metal case, Swedish, circa 1955. (Auction Team Köln) £89 $141

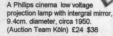

Oak cased barograph by Redferns of Sheffield, No. H11528, English, circa 1900. (G.A. Key) £330 $525

An 18th century English brass graphometer, the frame with two sights and double scales from 0 to 180 and 180 to 360 degrees, 22.5cm. wide. (Phillips) £4,370 $6,992

A late Victorian barograph, the seven stacking movement with brass fittings, in bevelled glazed mahogany framed case, 14¼in. wide. (Christie's) £552 $916

A Griffin & George, London, Wimshurst machine, gilt conductor balls and connections, on painted plywood base, circa 1950. (Auction Team Köln) £226 $373

An Augsburg brass equinoctial dial, by Lorenz Grassl, 18th century, square shaped plate engraved with foliate scrolls, cornucopia, birds and hounds, 3⅛in. square. (Sotheby's) £2,119 $3,162

Cased transit, marked *W. & L.E. Gurley, Troy, NY* and *C.C. Hutchinson, Boston, MA*, fitted case with accessories and tripod. (Eldred's) £252 $413

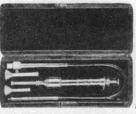

A late 18th century/early 19th century lacquered brass twin pillar double action vacuum pump, on a moulded mahogany base, 28cm. wide. (Phillips) £437 $699

A Read's patent hydraulic machine, English, second quarter, 19th century, with accessories in green plush lined morocco case, 23cm. (Bonhams) £120 $193

A tangential compass by Baird of Edinburgh, wooden, with brass compass housing, circa 11cm. diameter, circa 1890. (Auction Team Köln) £89 $142

The Original Knox Fluter fluting iron, with brass roll, American, circa 1880. (Auction Team Köln) £74 $122

A French iron doorknocker, 16th century, elaborately wrought in the form of two dolphins swallowing a bearded mask, knocker 5½in. long. (Sotheby's) £1,233 $1,840

A French steel doorknocker, late 16th century, the s-shaped body of an amphisbaena with grotesque masks knocker 7⅛in. long. (Sotheby's) £770 $1,150

A German Bolzen iron No.8 by L. Schröder, Schalksmühle, with ceramic handle, circa 1910. (Auction Team Köln) £164 $271

An extremely early French anvil, probably 16th century, museum quality. (Tool Shop Auctions) £1,350 $2,228

A Knox Imperial fluting iron with portrait photograph and floral decoration, American, 1877. (Auction Team Köln) £134 $213

An Adam style cast iron and brass fire grate, 19th century, the pedimented back above serpentine fronted basket, 74cm. wide. (Bristol) £460 $713

A cast-iron fireback, Pennsylvania, 18th century, of rectangular form depicting a minister in a pulpit with inscription below, 29¼in. wide. (Sotheby's) £1,085 $1,840

Mixed metal inlaid iron tetsuban with orchid design, Meiji period, the tall handled teapot finely finished with a deep chocolate brown patina, 7½in. high. (Butterfield & Butterfield) £862 $1,380

An Anker Heegaad heaxgonal cast iron iron stove, on three lion's paw feet, with five various irons. (Auction Team Köln) £264 $420

Large cast iron butterfly maedate, Edo period, constructed with two front and two back wings each pierced with three stylised prunus mon, 10¾in. high. (Butterfield & Butterfield) £1,617 $2,587

A Berlin cast carbon 'dragon' iron, plate 17cm. long, circa 1900. (Auction Team Köln) £98 $156

Diamond, cultured pearl, gold clip-brooch, featuring full-cut diamonds, set in 18ct white gold, enhanced by one cultured pearl. (Butterfield & Butterfield) £462 $748

Etruscan Revival lapis lazuli and gold bracelet, featuring five lapis lazuli cabochons, set in circular 15ct gold frames. (Butterfield & Butterfield) £2,365 $3,737

Diamond, sapphire, ruby, silver-topped gold brooch, featuring single-cut diamonds, enhanced by round-cut sapphires. (Butterfield & Butterfield) £3,549 $5,750

An 18ct. gold and synthetic ruby mounted spray brooch of stylised design, signed *Kutchinsky*. (Bearne's) £880 $1,426

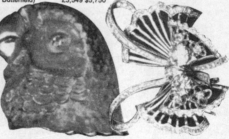

Multi-colour 14ct. gold brooch, designed as a parrot's head with textured feathers and a diamond-set eye, boxed. (Skinner) £551 $863

Diamond brooch, set with two diamonds, approx. total wt. 2.33cts., within a diamond openwork 14ct. white gold mount. (Skinner) £1,950 $3,105

18ct. yellow gold and sapphire brooch, designed as a frog set with sapphires, gold granulation accents, cabochon-cut ruby eyes, English hallmarks. (Skinner) £2,166 $3,450

A 19th century gold and rock crystal triple swivel seal of scroll design, the seal engraved with a crest, coat-of-arms and a monogram. (Bearne's) £480 $778

Marianne Brandt and Hin Bredendieck for Körting & Mathiesen AG, Leipzig, adjustable bedside lamp '702', 1928, brown lacquered steel, silver painted interior, black plastic, 12^2/₃in. max. height. (Sotheby's)　£414　$675

A bronze lamp in the form of sandalled foot, an aperture at the ankle decorated with calyx leaves, Roman, circa 1st–2nd century A.D., 4^3/₈in. long. (Bonhams)　£1,050　$1,669

Christian Dell for Zimmermann GmbH, Frankfurt am Main, table lamp 'Type K', 1929 black painted and nickel-plated steel, black painted iron sheet, 20^7/₈in. max. height. (Sotheby's)　£862　$1,405

Tiffany acorn desk lamp, leaded green and white glass segments with green-amber acorn-shaped leaf and vine border, 17in. high. (Skinner)　£2,911　$4,600

Tiffany Studios bronze and gold damascene piano lamp, ten prominent ribs in amber favrile glass shade with golden iridised damascene decoration, 9^1/₂in. diameter. (Skinner) £2,880 $4,600

Duffner Kimberly leaded glass lamp, sixteen-panel amber caramel slag conical shade with Prairie School-type gold square belt border, 23in. high. (Skinner)　£1,601　$2,530

Handel reverse painted scenic lamp, especially fine colourful riverside summer scene handpainted on glass dome shade, 22^1/₂in. high. (Skinner)　£2,911　$4,600

'Coupe Fleurie', a pâte de verre lamp, by Gabriel Argy-Rousseau, 1923, modelled as a cluster of stylised flowerheads, 5^5/₈in. high overall. (Christie's)　£6,095　$9,935

Rare Roycroft table lamp, four-sided trapezoidal shade with curvilinear supports and stepped base framing panels of slag glass, 26in. high. (Skinner)　£2,911　$4,600

A French white marble bust of Benjamin Franklin, after Jean-Antoine Houdon, 19th century, his head slightly bowed, 25¼in. high. (Sotheby's) £11,224 $18,400

A white marble group of Ganymede and the Eagle, after Bertel Thorvaldsen (Danish, 1770–1844), the youthful Ganymede wearing a Phrygian cap, 45cm. high. (Sotheby's) £5,175 $8,435

An Italian white marble bust of Apollo after the Antique, late 18th/19th century, on waisted marble socle, 26¾in. high. (Sotheby's) £5,261 $8,625

A large Italian marble group of Menelaus and Patroclus, after Pietro Tacca, the helmeted Greek hero dragging the dying, naked youth across the rocks, 49½in. high. (Sotheby's) £5,612 $9,200

An Italian marble baptismal font, 12th century, carved with rampant beasts and birds within interlocking circlets, 18⅞in. high. (Sotheby's) £6,549 $9,775

A white marble group of a bacchanalian dance, French, late 19th century, in the manner of Clodion (French, 1738–1814), 92cm. high. (Sotheby's) £20,700 $33,741

A marble bust of Jules Hardouin, after Antoine Coysevox (original 1698), late 19th/20th century, 34¾in. high. (Sotheby's) £2,542 $3,910

A fleur de pêcher centrepiece, Paris, circa 1880, the lobed body applied with scroll handles cast with foliage and bullrushes, 46cm. high. (Sotheby's) £8,625 $14,059

Italian carved Carrara marble bust of Venus, with clamshell, pearl headdress and shell covered bust, 25½in. high. (Skinner) £3,594 $5,750

A brass ship's bell, English, 1940s, with GVIR cypher and marked 3–5, with clapper, 24cm. diameter.
(Bonhams)   £130 $209

Two mahogany rudders, 20th century, each with brass mounts, largest 117cm.
(Bonhams)   £300 $482

A three-bolt Russian diving helmet, circa 1975, hand beaten with three face plates, each threaded, front with pags for removal, 19in. high.
(Christie's)   £2,070 $3,312

A Chadburn brass ship telegraph, English, 20th century, signed *Chadburns*, 80cm., together with a brass panel.
(Bonhams)   £500 $804

U-boat 20 Bell, the submarine responsible for the torpedoing of R.M.S. Lusitania in the spring of 1915.
(Christie's)   £13,800 $22,080

A Miller-Dunn Co. copper style II navy standard diving hood, American, 20th century, with brass angled glazed visor, arched shoulders air inlet and handle, 61cm. high.
(Bonhams)   £1,200 $1,929

A Henry Brown & Son brass compass binnacle, English, early 20th century, with 9cm floating compass rose, gimbal mount and brass housing, 30.5cm.
(Bonhams)   £220 $354

H.M.S. 'Britannia', a pair of tri-focal aluminium and leather binoculars signed on the eye-pieces J. *Coombs. Devonport*, 7½in. fully extended.
(Christie's)   £402 $643

A souvenir plate from S.S. Normandie designed and signed *R. Liftreau*, by Haviland of France, 9¾in. diameter.
(Christie's)   £345 $552

An unusual musical photograph album, playing 2 airs on a 32-tone comb, containing original photographs, circa 1880. (Auction Team Köln) £122 $194

A rare German Trombino silvered tin 18-tone mechanical trumpet, with 4 paper rolls, circa 1900. (Auction Team Köln) £698 $1,152

An Ariston tabletop wind-up organ for 29cm. cardboard discs, with 11 discs, German, circa 1895. (Auction Team Köln) £447 $711

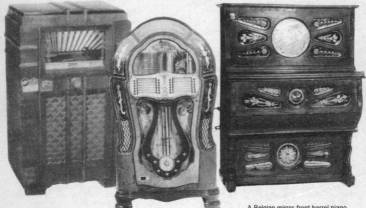

A Seeburg Symphonola Type B early juke box by the Seeburg Co. Chicago, Art Deco style wooden case, for 12 shellac discs, 1936. (Auction Team Köln) £739 $1,219

A Wurlitzer 1080 24 disc juke box, with a few discs, 1947. (Auction Team Köln) £6,101 $9,700

A Belgian mirror-front barrel piano, playing 10 different melodies, together with 8-tone xylophone and 3-tone Glockenspiel, 130cm. wide, circa 1900. (Auction Team Köln) £349 $576

A Baby Tanzbaer Concertina, by Zuleger, Leipzig, with external handle to advance the paper roll, circa 1900. (Auction Team Köln) £513 $846

A Q.R.S. Play-A-Sax mechanical saxophone with three rolls. (Auction Team Köln) £144 $238

A French musical box, with silvered brass case and brass handle with porcelain finial, circa 9cm. diameter. (Auction Team Köln) £81 $129

HISTORICAL FACTS
Mirrors

The earliest known mirrors, examples of which have survived to be found in Egyptian tombs, were fashioned simply as hand held discs of polished metal.

It was not until 1507 that the Venetian glassmakers of Murano applied a method of backing plain glass with an amalgam of mercury and tin. This backing was prone to flaking, causing distortion and spotting, but about a century later the technique of backing glass with mercury and tinfoil was adopted successfully in England giving rise to factory production and a healthy export trade throughout Europe.

When the Duke of Buckingham opened a glass factory at Vauxhall producing mirrors of a large size a trend was established for every household of note to hang those fine quality mirrors, some embellished with pictures superimposed on the glass and many in beautifully carved frames. Initially the most popular placing was over chimney pieces and between windows.

The 18th century saw the decline of the fashion for peering into tiny hand mirrors and the rise in popularity of a larger dressing table mirror. Swing dressing table mirrors and cheval mirrors too, were produced in great numbers.

Each succeeding fashion in furnishing had its equivalent style of mirror ranging from Chippendale gilded pine to Victorian gilt gesso frames and the beaten bronze of the Arts and Crafts period.

A classical carved pine giltwood convex mirror, possibly New York, circa 1825, the spreadwing eagle above a spherule-mounted circular frame, 4ft. 4in. high.
(Sotheby's)   £1,929 $3,162

A Regency mahogany, crossbanded and line inlaid dressing-table mirror, bowfront box-base fitted with three drawers, 21in. wide.
(Christie's)   £402 $663

A painted mirror frame, by Ben Nicholson, 1930, stained and painted with zig-zags, dots and stripes, 29 x 29in.
(Christie's)   £18,400 $29,992

A polychrome-decorated églomisé and red stained pine courting mirror, Continental, 18th/19th century, 17in. high.
(Sotheby's)   £374 $575

A Chinese-export black and gilt-lacquer dressing-mirror, 18th century, decorated overall with Chinese landscape scenes and foliage, 15in. wide.
(Christie's)   £747 $1,225

A 19th century Dieppe bone and ivory wall mirror with oval bevelled plate surrounded by foliage, cherubs and coats of arms, 33in. high.
(Ewbank)   £2,200 $3,520

A Waterman's 18ct. gold CF, with navy line and fluted design and medium 18ct. inlaid nib, London, 1973.
(Bonhams) £400 $660

CC/Waterman, a bi-colour 18ct. gold CF, with inlaid 18 medium nib, English, 1970s.
(Bonhams) £1,400 $2,352

Carey(?), a white metal filigree eyedropper, marked *Sterling* with no. 3 Carey nib, American, circa 1920.
(Bonhams) £190 $319

Parker, a 9ct. gold 'Waterdrop' 61, with 9ct gold clip cartridge/convertor filler, London, 1970.
(Bonhams) £300 $504

Wahl Eversharp, a pearl and black oversize Gold Seal Deco Band, with flexible Gold Seal nib, American, circa 1929. (Bonhams) £130 $218

A gold plated Waterman's 42 Safety, with detailed rose design, ring-top and No.2 nib, probably Italian, 1920s.
(Bonhams) £360 $594

Inkograph Co, a black Mickey Mouse pen, the barrel transfer decorated with a picture of Mickey, American circa 1935.
(Bonhams) £300 $504

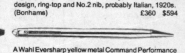

A Wahl Eversharp yellow metal Command Performance pen and pencil set, both marked 14ct. solid gold, pen with Skyline nib, American 1940s.
(Bonhams) £260 $429

A Mabie Todd and Bard gold plated 'Snail and Twist' Swan eyedropper, with under-over fed nib, American, circa 1910.
(Bonhams) £380 $627

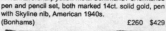

Mordan, a bone pen/pencil thermometer/compass combination, with engraved white metal mounts, the compass set into the finial, English, 1860s/1880s.
(Bonhams) £400 $672

Sheaffer, a limited edition W A Sheaffer Commemorative Pen no. 4787/6000, the brass, lever filling pen decorated with low relief foliate design and two-colour 18ct. nib, American, 1996.
(Bonhams) £260 $437

A Mont Blanc gold plated 0–M baby Safety, the barrel decorated with alternating columns of plain and wavy line design and with twin bands decorated with a blue enamelled floral pattern and with Mont Blanc '0' nib, German, circa 1920. (Bonhams) £1,100 $1,815

A Bion-pattern fountain pen, the brass body of tapered cylindrical form decorated with red hard wax and copper foil glass, both incorporating black 'dragged' lines, closed 125mm., probably French, but possibly English or Italian, mid 18th century.
(Bonhams) £1,800 $3,024

A Mont Blanc limited edition Lorenzo de Medici No.2734/4810, marked *925*, the black resin body covered by an octagonal overlay with alternating panels of engine turned and engraved design and with two-colour 18ct. 4810 nib, German, 1992.
(Bonhams) £3,600 $5,652

An unmarked pen holder, with tortoiseshell and piqué body decorated with flowers and plain holder, English, early 19th century.
(Bonhams) £260 $437

A yellow metal and glass pen holder and propelling pencil set, each with octagonal bodies decorated with a snake, with red stone eyes, the pen holder with sprung grip, English, circa 1900. (Bonhams) £280 $470

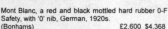

Mont Blanc, a red and black mottled hard rubber 0-F Safety, with '0' nib, German, 1920s.
(Bonhams) £2,600 $4,368

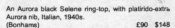

An Aurora black Selene ring-top, with platirido-extra Aurora nib, Italian, 1940s.
(Bonhams) £90 $148

Parker, a black 51 Aerometric with Betty Grable clip, American, 1950s. (Bonhams) £80 $134

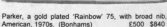

Parker, a gold plated 'Rainbow' 75, with broad nib, American, 1970s. (Bonhams) £500 $840

A pewter creamer, attributed to William Will, 1742–98, Philadelphia, with curved and beaded spout, 4½in. high.
(Christie's) £4,347 $6,900

An Art Nouveau pewter five-piece tea service in the "Orivit" pattern, comprising: hot-water jug, lidded sugar basin, and tea tray, tray 16¾in. long.
(Christie's) £402 $613

Liberty & Co. pewter owl pitcher, incised decoration with ceramic blue eyes, 8in. high.
(Skinner) £236 $373

Liberty & Co. Tudric pewter ice bucket, raised foliate design, impressed *Made In England, Tudric Pewter 0705*, 6in. high.
(Skinner) £467 $747

A pair of pewter candelabra, designed by Hugo Leven, manufactured by Kayserzinn, circa 1903, organic form with double branches, 10½in. high.
(Christie's) £2,760 $4,416

TOP TIPS
Auctioneer's Advice

A note of caution – whilst auctioneers do everything they can to protect the items sold, there are the occasional instances when items vanish after a sale.

Collect your purchased goods as soon as possible. Remember they are your responsibility once the gavel has fallen and are no longer covered by the auction room's insurance.

WHITWORTHS

An early 20th century pewter inkwell in the form of a 'Martin Brothers' grotesque bird with three legs, 11cm.
(Bearne's) £240 $388

A Modernist cocktail shaker, designed by Sylvia Stave, manufactured by Hallberg, Sweden, spherical with loop handle, 7¼in. high. (Christie's) £7,130 $10,624

A pewter teapot, by Liberty & Co., circa 1910, and a coffee pot, sugar basin and cream jug of similar form.
(Christie's) £103 $168

Robert Howlett (1831-58), Soldiers in front of a gun carriage at Greenwich Hospital 1855, light albumen print, 9¼ x 7⅜in., arched top, mounted on card.
(Christie's)　£805　$1,320

Benjamin Brecknell Turner (1815-94), 'Scotch Firs, Hawkhurst', circa 1852, albumen print from a waxed paper negative, 11¼ x 15⅜in.
(Christie's)　£21,850　$35,834

Richard Avedon, 'Carmen (Homage to Munkacsi), Paris, 1957', printed later, gelatin silver print, 18 x 14in., signed and numbered 17 on verso.
(Christie's)　£6,670　$10,939

Dorothea Lange (1895-1965), 'Bridie O'Halloran', 'Linked Hands', Ireland 1955, two gelatin silver prints, 10 x 7¾ and 8¼ x 8in.
(Christie's)　£1,035　$1,697

Bert Stern (born 1929), Marilyn Monroe, 1962, printed later, platinum print, image size 14½ x 22in. signed, dated and titled *Marilyn*. (Christie's)£1,955　$3,206

Jeremiah Gurney, Portrait of two children, 1850s, daguerreotype, 5 x 4in., delicately hand-tinted, gilt matt with arched corners.
(Christie's)　£977　$1,602

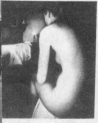

Charles Jones, 'Bean Runner', circa 1900, gelatin silver print, 10 x 8in., signed C.J., titled and annotated in pencil on verso.
(Christie's)　£1,610　$2,640

Jacques-Henri Lartigue, 'Promeneuses (Avenue du Bois), Bois de Boulogne', 1915, gelatin silver print, 4½ x 4¹¹/₁₆in., dated later in pencil on verso.
(Christie's)　£11,500　$18,860

Bill Brandt (1904-83), 'Nude, Campden Hill', London, 1949, printed later, gelatin silver print, 13½ x 11½in., surmounted on card, signed in ink on mount.
(Christie's)　£1,495　$2,392

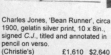

HISTORICAL FACTS
Advertising Posters

The process of colour lithography and the importance attached to advertising in the 1890s led to a flourishing of artistic posters and include the work of leading Parisian artists Cheret, Toulouse-Lautrec and Bonnard. French posters of this period for theatre, cycles, cigarettes and drink range from around £200 to several thousands of pounds depending on the artists and graphics.

Shell-Mex and BP adopted an unusual way of displaying posters. Their vehicles were fitted with display boards to which these 'lorry bills' measuring 76 x 102cm. were fixed Between 1920 and 1939 five hundred and forty-five designs were published. The Visit Britain's Landmarks series with the slogan 'Everywhere You Go You Can Be Sure Of Shell' included Rye Marshes and Kimmeridge Folly by Paul Nash, The Great Globe, Swanage by Graham Sutherland, Farringdon Folly by Lord Berners, Swaledale, Yorkshire by Barnett Freedman and many others. Average price is around £200–400 but more for certain artists designs. A series known as 'These Men Use Shell' included Journalists by Hans Schleger, Footballers by Paul Nash, Theatregoers by John Armstrong, Actors by E McKnight Kauffer, Racing Motorists by Richard Guyatt and Airmen by Andrew Johnson. Most of these are in the £800–£1,500 price range.

John Jenkins (Onslow's)

After E. Vulliement, Cycles Peugeot, lithograph in colours, circa 1910, printed by L. Revon & Cie, Paris, backed on linen, 63½ x 47in.
(Christie's)   £460 $736

Anonymous, Vermouth Perucchi, lithograph in colours, circa 1935, printed by J. Ortega, Valencia, backed on linen, 42 x 30in.
(Christie's)   £230 $368

Fraikin, Ce Michelin est Indechirable, lithograph in colours, 1908, printed by Ch. Verneau, Paris, backed on linen, 35½ x 30in.
(Christie's)   £1,150 $1,840

Anonymous, Michelin, Confort-Bibendum, lithograph in colours, circa 1930, backed on linen, 77 x 49in.
(Christie's)   £977 $1,563

Anonymous, Rosee Creme, lithograph in colours, circa 1900, printed by Charles Verneau, Paris, 55 x 39½in.
(Christie's)   £299 $478

Georges Dola (1872–1950), Kina-Lillet, lithograph in colours, circa 1900, printed by Imprimeries Reunies de Levallois, backed on linen, 55 x 38½in.
(Christie's)   £299 $478

A pieced cotton coverlet, signed *Sarah E. Bosworth, Bristol, Rhode Island*, circa 1883, worked in various coloured calicos and chintzes, in 144 squares each in the Kansas sunflower pattern, 88¼ x 88¼in.
(Christie's) £1,159 $1,840

Hooked bed rug, probably northern New England, 19th century, loose weave butternut dyed wool ground with hooked wool floral design in green, cerise, and coral, 80 x 70in.
(Skinner) £366 $575

A pieced and appliqued cotton quilted coverlet, Pennsylvania, third quarter 19th century, worked in red, green and yellow solids and calico cottons in the Harvest Sun pattern, 86 x 86in. (Christie's) £869 $1,380

A pieced and appliqued cotton crib quilt, American, circa 1845–55, worked pink, red, blue, green and mustard cottons and calicos in the Star of Bethlehem pattern, 46¼ x 47½in. (Christie's) £1,594 $2,530

A pieced and appliquéd cotton quilted coverlet, Pennsylvania, circa 1865, worked in the Star of Bethlehem pattern, 75in. x 74in.
(Christie's) £2,243 $3,450

A fine pieced and appliquéd cotton quilt top, Arthur Schuman, Berne, Berks County, Pennsylvania, late 19th century, approx. 80in. x 80in.
(Sotheby's) £285 $460

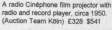

An Ozarka Senior American 5 valve battery radio, circa 1925.
(Auction Team Köln) £203 $323

A Seibt EA381 radio with original valves, 1930.
(Auction Team Köln) £976 $1,552

A radio Cinéphone film projector with radio and record player, circa 1950.
(Auction Team Köln) £328 $541

A Zenith Model K 725 7-valve, 110v, bakelite radio, with built-in aerial, circa 1945.
(Auction Team Köln) £41 $65

A Philco Transitone Model 49-602 portable battery radio, 4 valves, circa 1945.
(Auction Team Köln) £28 $45

A Telefunken 230W 'cat's head' radio, in good original condition, circa 1933.
(Auction Team Köln) £203 $323

A Bajazzo 51 Telefunken portable 3-band radio, battery or mains powered, circa 1951.
(Auction Team Köln) £73 $116

A Blaupunkt B VII 3-valve battery radio with Blaupunkt reels, valves replaced, 1928/9.
(Auction Team Köln) £1,220 $1,940

A Zenith Model 6 Y 001 portable radio with 6-valve battery and mains receiver, circa 1943.
(Auction Team Köln) £41 $65

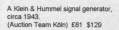

A Mende Type M 169/35 bakelite 3-valve radio with wave trap, 1935.
(Auction Team Köln) £62 $102

National Panasonic for Matsushita Electric Industrial Co. Ltd., Japan, portable radio model 'R-725', circa 1969, plastic.
(Sotheby's) £115 $187

A Klein & Hummel signal generator, circa 1943.
(Auction Team Köln) £81 $129

A distinctive black wool top hat worn by Guns n' Roses guitarist Slash, signed in gold marker, *Slash '94*. (Christie's)   £841 $1,380

The Beatles, the album 'Yesterday And Today', 1966, Capitol Records, stereo, T2553, with 'Butcher' cover, 12½ x 12½in. (Christie's)   £667 $1,093

A black satin and lycra bustier with front hook closure, ribbed back and elastic straps made for Madonna, with a letter of provenance. (Christie's)   £4,209 $6,900

A suit worn by Elton John in the music video for 'Don't Go Breaking My Heart', his duet with singer Kiki Dee. (Christie's)   £3,507 $5,750

A 1964 set of four Beatles Dolls, wearing black suits with trademark bowl-style haircuts, with facsimile signatures in gold, 5in. (Christie's)   £701 $1,150

A circa early 1950s, tobacco sunburst finish, acoustic Southern Jumbo Gibson guitar, serial no. Z193328, owned and played by Hank Williams. (Christie's)   £68,625 $112,500

A circa 1970s black and white poster of Van Morrison, pictured with guitar, signed in blue ink, 34 x 22½in., framed. (Christie's)   £246 $403

(What's The Story) Morning Glory?, C.D., inside booklet signed in black felt tip by Liam, Noel Gallagher, Bonehead, Paul McGuigan and Alan White. (Bonhams) £320 $512

A trademark work shirt worn by Bob Marley during his TUFF GOING UPRISING tour, the circa 1980 shirt is of heavy blue denim with front white metal snap closures. (Christie's)   £4,209 $6,900

HISTORICAL FACTS
Sewing Machines

The familiar lockstitch sewing machine was invented by an American machinist, Elias Howe in 1846, and patented by Isaac Merrit Singer in 1851. In the years that followed, many firms tried to cash in on this wonderful new device, but it was the Singer Sewing Machine Co. which cornered the lion's share of the market. By 1890 they turned out 10 million machines, many of which were of such high quality that they are still usable today.

The sewing machine boom even generated the spin-off invention of the sewing machine chair, a collectable in its own right, which was patented in 1871.

Collecting early machinery is becoming increasingly popular, and the sewing machine is one of the favourites. There are enough of them around and they are by and large still affordable. Above all, they have an aesthetic appeal all of their own, for many early examples are beautifully made and wonderfully embellished with gilt and mother of pearl, inlay, or even hand painting.

Early machines to look out for apart from Singer's are the Imperial Sewing Co of Birmingham; the Howe Sewing Machine Co; those imported from Germany by J. Collier and Son of Clapham Road, London; Wright and Mann of Ipswich and the small chain stitch machines sold by James Weir of Soho Square which were pirated copies of earlier machines made in Canada by Charles Raymond.

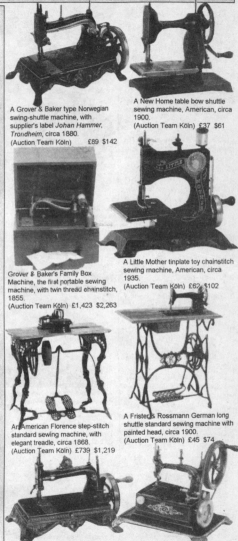

A Grover & Baker type Norwegian swing-shuttle machine, with supplier's label *Johan Hammer, Trondheim*, circa 1880.
(Auction Team Köln)   £89 $142

A New Home table bow shuttle sewing machine, American, circa 1900.
(Auction Team Köln) £37 $61

Grover & Baker's Family Box Machine, the first portable sewing machine, with twin thread chainstitch, 1855.
(Auction Team Köln) £1,423 $2,263

A Little Mother tinplate toy chainstitch sewing machine, American, circa 1935.
(Auction Team Köln) £62 $102

An American Florence step-stitch standard sewing machine, with elegant treadle, circa 1868.
(Auction Team Köln) £739 $1,219

A Frister & Rossmann German long shuttle standard sewing machine with painted head, circa 1900.
(Auction Team Köln) £45 $74

An original Brunonia German swing shuttle sewing machine by Bremer and Brückmann, Braunschweig, with shuttle, 1895.
(Auction Team Köln)   £66 $109

A very rare Swedish swing shuttle machine by Öller, Stockholm, forerunner of L.M. Ericsson, circa 1865.
(Auction Team Köln) £894 $1,422

HISTORICAL FACTS
Coffee Pots

Coffee pots were first introduced about 1680, and the earliest were straight-sided, tapering forms, which a little later became polygonal. Pear-shaped bodies were first introduced about 1730 and the Adam period heralded classical vase forms. Continental pots were normally vase-shaped, and many had highly exotic decoration. In America, the shape followed the English style at first, with a severely tapering form, being modified about 20 years later to become rounded at the base, on a narrow, moulded foot. American rococo examples were pear-shaped and tall, with a domed cover, while in the Federal period an inverted pear-shape was preferred, with a simple scroll wooden handle. Side handles went out of fashion about 1715.

In England, no coffee pots made before 1730 are embossed or engraved, apart from armorials. (A good armorial can make a big difference to the value.) From 1730–40 there may be some flat-chasing, but it was not until 1740–60 that any embossing occurs. If the decoration is floral, it seldom covers more than two-thirds of the surface area. Overall floral decoration, especially on a matted background, is more characteristic of the Victorian era. Between 1780 and 1815 engraving usually consists of bright-cut decorative borders, with beading coming in during the early part of that period followed by thread borders in the 1790s.

Fine early 19th century child's large silver whistle/rattle/teether, (one bell missing), 6in. long, maker J.F. (G.A. Key)   £230 $361

A silver-plated wine trolley, 19th century, on four spoked wheels and with vine tendril handle, the double coaster with basketwork sides, 19¼in. long.
(Christie's)   £920 $1,536

A Victorian plated and electro-gilt mounted brandy dispenser, late 19th century, fitted with two staved and hooped cut glass barrels with detachable mounted cork stoppers, 10½in. wide.
(Christie's)   £517 $853

A Fabergé circular cigar cutter in silver gilt and blue basse taille, enamel painted with trailing leafage frieze in white, 1.6in. diameter.
(Russell Baldwin & Bright)
                              £7,200 $11,520

A Continental model of a standing cockerel with detachable head, realistically modelled with textured feathers and comb, by B. Muller, English import marks for 1910, 23cm high, (on wooden base), 23.5oz. (Christie's)   £632 $1,046

Fine Edwardian large silver biscuit barrel, the lid with pomegranate finials, 7in. high, London 1902 by the Goldsmiths and Silversmiths Co., 22oz. (G. A. Key)   £380 $608

A modern three-piece condiment set of shaped oval form with pierced and bright-cut decoration, blue glass liners and spoons, Birmingham 1976.
(Bearne's)   £190 $308

Unusual hallmarked silver pouring vessel in Turkish style with animal head handle, beaded detail, Chester 1910, 7oz.
(G.A. Key)   £140 $223

A French circular wine taster with ring handle with initialled thumbpiece, 11.5cm. long.
(Bearne's) £120 $194

Heavy silver pap boat of usual form with lined rim and bearing a crest, London, probably 1768.
(G.A. Key) £200 $318

Interesting Georgian silver lemon strainer, circular shaped with stylised floral piercing, maker's mark *M.B.*
(G.A. Key) £250 $397

A Scottish silver mounted ram's head table snuff mull, maker's mark *J.K.*, Edinburgh, 1860, the full ram's head on three brass mounted wood castors, 16in. wide.
(Christie's) £5,175 $8,590

Silver and shakudo reticulate study of a dragonfly, elegantly rendered with silver wings and shakudo body, signed under one wing *Muneyoshi*, 3⁷/₈in. long.
(Butterfield & Butterfield) £1,797 $2,875

A pair of George III nut crackers, crested, John Shea, London 1807, 116gm., 3.7oz.
(Bearne's) £410 $664

A Victorian silver mounted heart-shaped mirror, the frame chased and pierced with putti and birds, 28.5cm. high, William Comyns, 1898.
(Bearne's) £500 $810

A pair of George I silver tazze, Paul de Lamerie, London, 1720, each on detachable spreading foot with baluster stem, 6¼in. diameter, 25oz.
(Christie's) £21,850 $36,053

A large tazza, designed by Georg Jensen, circa 1918, manufactured 1915/27, deep bowl with clusters of grapes below, 10¹/₂in. high.
(Christie's) £4,370 $7,123

A Dutch silver large model of a pheasant, 1924, realistically modelled with boot button eyes, 25oz., 21in. long.
(Sotheby's) £1,052 $1,725

A pair of Chilean spurs, dated *1913*, low grade silver inlay on iron.
(Bonhams) £220 $357

Hallmarked silver memorial bell, well chased and embossed with religious figures and animals, 4in. high, London 1919, by C. Krall.
(G.A. Key) £250 $412

HISTORICAL FACTS
Teddy Bears

Most people are now familiar with the account of how the Teddy bear got its name. This tells how, while on a hunting trip in 1902, President Theodore Roosevelt could not bring himself to shoot a bear cub which had been conveniently tethered to a post by some well-meaning aide (the President having just shot its mother). Such fore'bear'ance on the part of the noted hunter appealed to the popular press, and the incident was captured in a cartoon of the day. Seeing this, one Morris Michtom, of the Ideal Toy Corp. who had created some toy bears, asked permission to call them after Theodore, so the Teddy bear came into being.

Roosevelt obviously felt the connection did no harm to the presidential image, and when his daughter married in 1906, the wedding breakfast tables were decorated with tiny bears made by the Steiff toy company.

Margrete Steiff had been making felt animals at Geingen in Germany for some time and was joined in 1897 by her ambitious nephew Richard. They exhibited at the Leipzig Fair in 1903 and the popularity of their toys was so great that the factory simply could not keep up with demand.

Pre-1910 Steiff bears tend to be rather elongated, with pointed snouts and humps. The Steiffs had the good marketing sense to put a characteristic button in each of their product's ears, thus making them instantly recognisable.

A Steiff teddy bear with golden mohair, black shoe button eyes, swivel head, jointed shaped limbs, 12½in. tall, circa 1905.
(Christie's)   £1,995 $3,162

A Merrythought teddy bear, with golden mohair, pronounced clipped snout, black stitched nose, mouth and claws, 17in. tall, 1930s.
(Christie's)   £173 $280

An early German teddy bear with golden mohair, black boot button eyes, centre facial seam, pronounced clipped snout, 19in. tall, circa 1910.
(Christie's)   £748 $1,210

A Steiff teddy bear with golden mohair, brown and black glass eyes, pronounced snout, hump and button in ear, 1920s, 16in. high.
(Christie's)   £1,035 $1,656

A French teddy bear with pale golden mohair, clear and black glass eyes painted on reverse, 29in. tall, 1930s.
(Christie's)   £230 $372

A Steiff teddy bear with golden mohair, black shoe button eyes, pronounced clipped snout, 12in. tall, circa 1905.
(Christie's)   £1,495 $2,418

Fireman William Nutbeam (Survivor), his Continuous Certificate of Discharge No. 680419, date of last ontry 8th June 1923. (Onslow's) £1,600 $2,500

A circular bakelite White Star Line ashtray, Omniteware made by Fraser & Glass London N8, 15cm diameter. (Onslow's) £95 £152

A Titanic memorial picture, Titanic photographed from a three quarter port bow position, 11½ x 16½in. (Christie's) £1,380 $2,208

A paper souvenir napkin, *In Affectionate Remembrance of the 1503 Persons Who Lost Their Lives by the Foundering of the World's Largest Liner SS Titanic*, with vignette of the Ship, 37cm. square, framed. (Onslow's) £150 $240

White Star Line TSS Titanic colour art postcard, from Thomas Mudd to his mother, '*Dear Mother, Arrived at Southampton safe The Titanic is a splendid boat*'.
(Onslow's) £3,600 $5,760

Titanic, hardback edition of Sinking of the Titanic, ed. by Marshall Everett, 13th May 1912. (Vennett-Smith) £105 $173

Postcard of 'SS Titanic foundered April 14th 1912 Over 1600 passengers drowned', mono art published by W & T Gaines. (Onslow's) £170 $272

On Board RMS Titanic, an unused perforated letter card with printed company burgee. (Onslow's) £950 $1,520

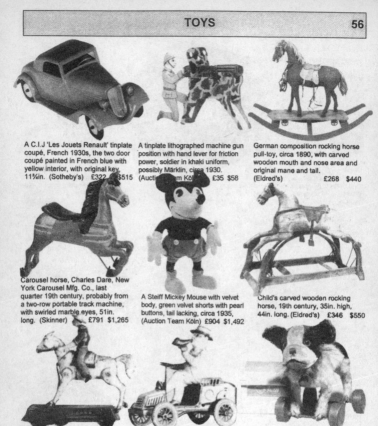

A C.I.J 'Les Jouets Renault' tinplate coupé, French 1930s, the two door coupé painted in French blue with yellow interior, with original key, 11¾in. (Sotheby's) £322 $515

A tinplate lithographed machine gun position with hand lever for friction power, soldier in khaki uniform, possibly Märklin, circa 1930. (Auction Team Köln) £35 $58

German composition rocking horse pull-toy, circa 1890, with carved wooden mouth and nose area and original mane and tail. (Eldred's) £268 $440

Carousel horse, Charles Dare, New York Carousel Mfg. Co., last quarter 19th century, probably from a two-row portable track machine, with swirled marble eyes, 51in. long. (Skinner) £791 $1,265

A Steiff Mickey Mouse with velvet body, green velvet shorts with pearl buttons, tail lacking, circa 1935, (Auction Team Köln) £904 $1,492

Child's carved wooden rocking horse, 19th century, 35in. high, 44in. long. (Eldred's) £346 $550

A Lehmann EPL 625 'Wild West', German, 1909-1945, the clockwork toy handpainted with white horse and rider with red shirt, 7½in. (Soth...) £230 $368

A Lehmann EPL 490 'Tut-Tut', German, 1903-1935, the clockwork car with bellows lithographed in cream and red, with matching driver, 6¾in. long. (Sotheby's) £575 $920

Steiff 'Bully' on wheels with black and white mohair, swivel head, horse hair collar, original bell and swing tag, 9in. long, circa 1929. (Christie's) £345 $558

A tinplate lithographed clockwork figure of a dwarf riding a snail, German, possibly Georg Köhler, circa 1950. (Auction Team Köln) £173 $285

Li'l Abner and his Dogpatch Band, American tinplate clockwork toy by Unique Art, in original box, 1945. (Auction Team Köln) £247 $408

A Wolverine 'Sunny Andy' Zilotone toy, American, circa 1931, the tinplate clockwork toy with curved gold and blue xylophone, played by a tinplate figure, 8¾in. long. (Sotheby's) £345 $552

HISTORICAL FACTS
Typewriters

It was as far back as 1714 that an Englishman, Henry Mill, first took out a patent for 'An Artificial Machine or Method for the Impression or Transcribing of Letters Singly or Progressively one after another, as in writing, whereby all Writing whatever may be Engrossed in Paper or Parchment so Neat and Exact as not to be distinguished form Print'. His design never went into production however, and it was not until nearly 130 years later, in 1843, the American Charles Thurber in turn patented his idea of a mechanical typewriter. From then on the concept really caught the imagination of inventors and there were numerous attempts to produce readable copy. None were successful however until, in 1867, the first practical typewriter was invented by three Americans, Sholes, Glidden and Soule. Their machine worked on a shift key mechanism, which forms the basis of more modern machines. Early typewriters demand good prices and are still to be found, mainly because of the enormous output of early manufacturers to cope with the immediate demand. In the 1870s alone, the companies of Remington, Oliver, Smith, Underwood and Yost sold over 50,000 models.

German machines by companies such as Edelmann are rarer as is the Gühl and Harbeck Kosmopolit typewriter with gilt and black finish and in a walnut case.

An American Index pointer typewriter, lacks rubber type, cylinder and type sheet, 1893.
(Auction Team Köln) £107 $177

An Elliott Fisher overstrike typesetting machine, American 1896.
(Auction Team Köln) £493 $813

A Typo typewriter, the French version of the decorative English type-bar machine, with round Ideal keyboard and double shift-key, 1914.
(Auction Team Köln) £452 $746

A Typo Visible French edition of the popular British Imperial Visible Model B, French Ideal keyboard with double shift key, 1914.
(Auction Team Köln) £411 $678

A Smith Premier No. 1., the first version of the decorative American understrike machine with full keyboard, with integral type cleaning brush, 1889.
(Auction Team Köln) £493 $813

A cast-iron based Sun Typewriter, one of the first pointer typewriters and forerunner of the Odell, 1885.
(Auction Team Köln) £1,098 $1,746

A Blickensdörfer No. 5 popular American type-wheel portable typewriter with early metal type board and original wooden case, 1893.
(Auction Team Köln) £90 $149

A de-luxe gold version of the Royal Quiet Deluxe typewriter, designed by Henry Dreyfuss, in original case, 1948.
(Auction Team Köln) £569 $905

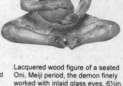

A Flemish oak relief of the adoration of the Magi, mid-16th century, one king kneeling before the Child kissing His hand, 33⅝in. x 26¼in. (Sotheby's) £9,717 $14,950

A pair of George III mahogany candlesticks on spiral twist tapered columns carved with acanthus leaves, 12¾in. high. (Anderson & Garland)
£190 $298

Lacquered wood figure of a seated Oni, Meiji period, the demon finely worked with inlaid glass eyes, 6½in. high. (Butterfield & Butterfield)
£719 $1,150

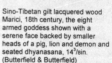

A Venetian painted wood Commedia dell'arte mask, 18th century, with long curved nose 5¾in. high. (Sotheby's) £1,929 $3,162

A South German (probably Ulm) painted wood relief of 'Noli me tangere' circa 1500, the Magdalene on the right kneeling before Christ, 32½ x 22½in. (Sotheby's) £11,925 $19,550

Sino-Tibetan gilt lacquered wood Marici, 18th century, the eight armed goddess shown with a serene face backed by smaller heads of a pig, lion and demon and seated dhyanasana, 14³/₈in. (Butterfield & Butterfield)
£1,438 $2,300

Lacquered wood figural study, depicting a bald elderly figure wearing an elaborately decorated robe, 2⅞in. high. (Butterfield & Butterfield) £503 $805

A pair of South German gilt and painted three-quarter length wood figures of Saints Barbara and Agnes early 16th century, 10in. and 9½in. (Sotheby's) £1,473 $2,415

A carved and painted model of an Indian elephant, 20th century, with two big ears and a long trunk, 54in. long. (Christie's) £1,955 $3,138

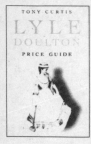

The Complete Decorator
Kevin McCloud   rrp £15.00
TV's Kevin McCloud has put together an unrivalled decorating reference book. With step by step photographs on the pro's techniques, a unique colour selector chart to make sure you get the tone you really want, and over 400 full colour photographs, *The Complete Decorator* is an essential addition to any decorator's library.
Special Offer Price £12.00 (+99p UK p&p)

Grand Illusions - New Decorating
Nick Ronald & David Roberts   rrp £19.99

Grand Illusions New Decorating is practical and inspirational. By taking different styles from the four corners of the globe, this fully illustrated volume gives you the essentials to achieve the perfect style for your home. If you are after Scandinavian chic, or, - who knows? - a room with a touch of the Orient, then *Grand Illusions New Decorating* will tell you exactly how to transform your home into a space of dreams.
Special Offer Price £15.99 (+99p UK p&p)

To order call 0181 324 5538 or post the form below to PL&TH Bookshop, 250 Western Avenue, London, W3 6EE.
Please place your order soon - special offer ends 1.11.98

❏ **The Complete Decorator**, *Kevin McCloud* @ £12.99 inc. UK p& (rrp £15.00)

❏ **Grand Illusions New Decorating** @ £16.98 inc. UK p&p (rrp £19.99)

❏ I enclose a UK cheque payable to *Period Living Bookshop* for £..............

❏ Please charge £..............to my Mastercard, Visa, Switch Card No.

⌐ˌ ˌ ˌ ˌ ˌ ˌ ˌ ˌ ˌ ˌ ˌ ˌ ˌ ˌ ˌ ˌ¬

Switch Issue No. ....   Card expiry date ..../.........

Name...

Address...

....

....

Postcode .... Telephone

Signature...
❏ Please do not send mailings from companies selected by Period Living Bookshop